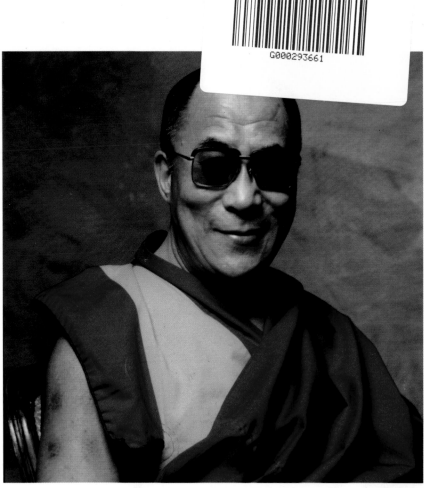

HH The DALAI LAMA

Stories have been the means of conveying common wisdom from one generation to another since time immemorial. We find that folk stories from all over the world are similar in containing a moral, a piece of advice, that shows us how to be better human beings, how to be more compassionate and concerned with others.

Tibetans have always been fond of telling stories and even fonder of listening to them. We have a rich store of folk-tales, most of which have not even been written down, let alone published. Therefore it is a pleasure to know that Ringu Tulku and Pankaj Thapa have prepared an illustrated edition of a Tibetan tale entitled *The Boy Who Had a Dream*. I hope that the children who read it will enjoy it and that it will lead them to take further interest in the Tibetan people and their culture.

March 21, 1995

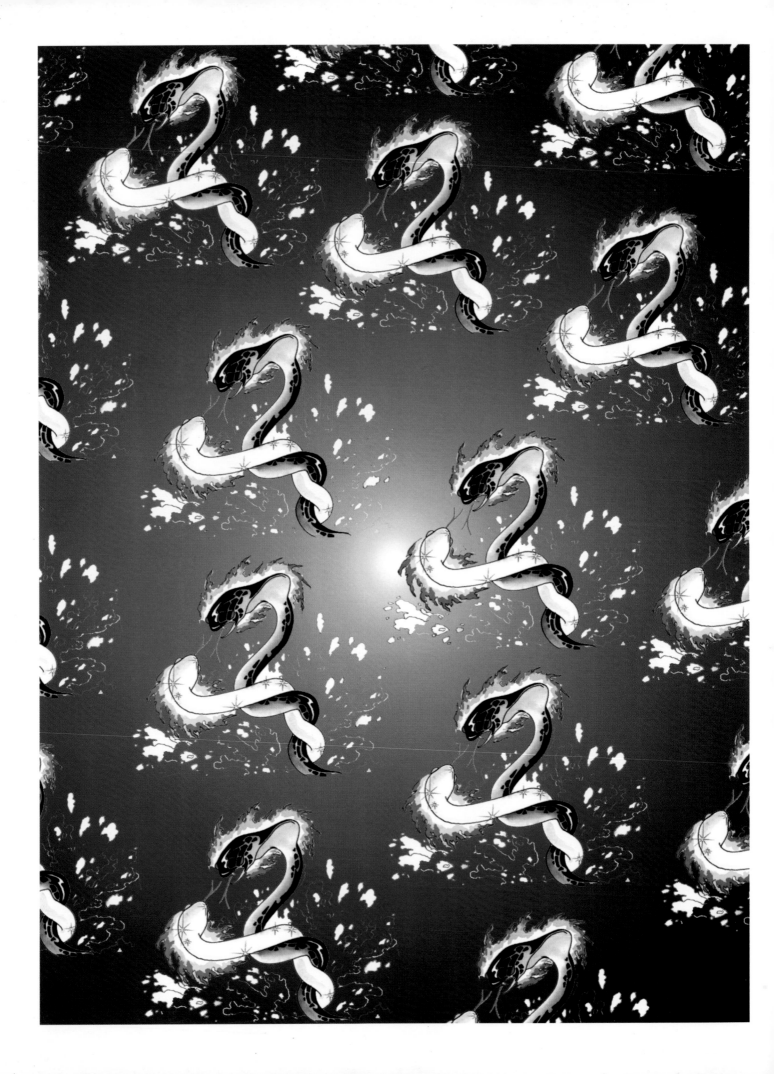

RINGU TULKU Rinpoche

Dear Reader,

I am delighted to be able to share this Tibetan folk tale with you. Perhaps this is the first time that the story is told in any language other than Tibetan. I first heard this story from my eighty-nine year-old great-aunt when I was about three years old. Since then, it has become one of my favourite stories and I never tired of listening to it again and again. I have told this story countless times both in the east and west. Children of all ages have enjoyed listening to it.

These stories helped me on many occasions in my childhood. They kept me cheerful when I had to travel night after night in rain, gale or under gun fire when we were escaping from Tibet. These stories gave me a right perspective to life so that I was not too much overwhelmed by many tragic changes in my life. I hope this story will not only entertain you but also help you in the way it helped me. You will certainly enjoy the beautiful illustrations made by Pankaj Thapa to whom I owe my deepest gratitude.

The money I receive from selling this book will go to a project in helping to educate the children in Kham, where my monastery is situated. I am confident that you would like to help by purchasing this book and recommending it to others.

Ringu Tulku

AMDO

TAKSTER

Kokonor KUMBUM

GOLMUD

T I B E T

Anye Machin Range

DERGE

U - T S A N G

Nam Tso

The Potala

KHAM

LHASA

Tsangpo

GYANTSE Yamdrok
Tso

NEPAL

(KATHMANDU)

SIKKIM BHUTAN

Brahmaputra

INDIA

(Map not to scale)

Pankaj

ABOUT TIBET

Since this story comes from Tibet, you might like to know something about the country. Tibet is often called 'The Roof of the World' because it is the highest country on our planet. The Tibetan plateau is about a million square miles shaped somewhat like an ankle-boot and it is surrounded by the world's highest snow mountains. The great Himalayan range forms its southern border. Tibet is the source of many important rivers in Asia such as the Brahmaputra, the Ganges, the Indus, the Yellow river, the Yalong, the Yangtse and the Mekong among others. This land was so protected by natural barriers that it developed and retained a distinct ancient culture which was unknown to the rest of the world until recently.

Tibet was rich in its wildlife, as its vast and varied landscape was sparsely populated. Wild yak, blue sheep, giant panda, wild ass, Tibetan gazelle, snow leopard, grizzly bear and many other wild animals roamed the wide open spaces of the plateau. The legendary yeti and snow lion are also believed to inhabit the highest regions of Tibet.

Due to its high altitude people tend to think that Tibet is an arid and barren land but large areas of Tibet have greenery and heavy vegetation. There are valleys which are thickly forested and have rhododendrons and wild flowers of every colour. Many medicinal plants and miraculous herbs are found everywhere. The unique Tibetan medical system had developed a profound knowledge of these herbal medicines.

The Tibetan society was made up of Drokpas and Yulpas. Drokpas are the nomads, and are sometimes referred to as the 'People of the Black Tents'. They graze their herds of yaks and sleep in remote valleys and get most of their requirements from their animals, such as cheese, meat, yoghurt, sheepskin clothes, boots of yak leather and tents of yak hair. They used dried yak dung as fuel and move camp by tying everything onto the yaks strong backs. The Drokpas barter animal products for grain and tea with the Yulpas who cultivate the land. This story is based on the Drokpa way of life in the region of Kham in eastern Tibet.

People of Tibet adopted Buddhism as their spiritual path in the eighth century and since then they have continuously explored the inner world in order to find a way out of human suffering.

There has been a great destruction of Tibetan religion, culture and natural environment in recent years. However, the people of Tibet and their friends outside Tibet are trying their best to revive and preserve its ancient civilisation and peaceful environment.

THE BOY WHO HAD A Dream

RINGU
TULKU
Rinpoche

PANKAJ
THAPA
illustrator

FINDHORN
Press

The Venerable **RINGU TULKU** Rinpoche is a Tibetan Buddhist monk recognised in his childhood as the rebirth of the Abbot of Rigul Monastery in eastern Tibet. Born in 1952 he was brought up in Sikkim by Khenpo Lama Rinchen according to the Tibetan tradition. He also studied at the Young Lamas Home School, Dalhousie; Namgyal Institute of Tibetology, Gangtok; and Sampurnananda Sanskrit University, Varanasi, where he received a masters degree in Buddhist Studies. He was awarded a doctoral degree by the Nyimgma School of Tibetan Buddhism and the title of Khenpo [Professor who gives ordinations] by the Kugyu School of Tibetan Buddhism. Ringu Tulku wrote a series of Tibetan textbooks for the schools of Sikkim and collated folktales and folklore for eight years between 1969 and 1987. Among his publications is a collection of Tibetan folktales. He has been a professor of Tibetan Studies in Sikkim for the last seventeen years. He founded the Sikkim Buddhist Association and published two annual buddhist journals as well as Buddhist texts for the colleges in India. For the last few years, he has been teaching Buddhism and meditation in the UK, Europe, USA and Australia. This book is for children of all ages from very young to those in their old age. The proceeds from this book will be dedicated to helping provide better education for the inhabitants of Rigul in Eastern Tibet.

PANKAJ THAPA is the Head of the Department of English at Sikkim Government College, and a well-known graphic designer and illustrator in Sikkim. He was born in 1960 in Dehradun, and educated at St. Edmund's School and College in Shillong. He post-graduated in English literature from the North-Eastern Hill University at Shillong, and did a stint of journalism before taking up teaching as a career. He has been teaching English literature and language in Sikkim since 1984.

Drawing is a natural talent for Pankaj and he has contributed his sketches and designs to many journals, newspapers and advertisements. He has also been appointed as a judge by the Sikkim Sahitya Parishad, and the Sikkim Academy of Fine Arts for their State and National level competitions.

THE BOY WHO HAD A Dream

ONCE UPON A TIME, IN A SMALL KINGDOM IN TIBET, RULED A KING NAMED CHAKA-GYALPO.

BUT HE WAS NOT A VERY GOOD KING, AND BECAUSE OF THIS, HE WAS DISLIKED BY HIS PEOPLE.

BEGONE! YOU PEASANT!

I KNEW IT!

NEAR THE KING'S PALACE WAS A SMALL HUT, WHERE A LITTLE BOY NAMED PHU-CHUNG LIVED WITH HIS WIDOWED MOTHER.

BEGONE! YOU PEASANT!

PHU-CHUNG, BEHAVE YOURSELF!

SHE WAS A KIND, GENTLE LADY, WHO WORKED VERY HARD TO MAKE ENDS MEET, AND FEED HER LITTLE BOY.

AS PHU-CHUNG GREW UP, HE WAS ABLE TO HELP HER WITH THE DAILY CHORES AND MAKE HER BURDEN LIGHTER...

ONE NIGHT AS HE LAY SLEEPING AFTER A HARD DAY'S WORK, HE HAD A STRANGE DREAM...

HE DREAMT THAT HE WAS WEARING A CROWN, AND SITTING ON THE THRONE. HE WAS RICHLY DRESSED, AND AROUND HIS NECK WAS A NECKLACE WITH NUMEROUS "ZEES"...

MOTHER, I HAD A WONDERFUL DREAM! I DREAMT I WAS THE KING, AND WAS SITTING ON THE THRONE!

O, MOTHER! PLEASE DON'T TELL ANYONE ABOUT MY DREAM. THE KING MAY NOT LIKE IT.

BUT PHU-CHUNG'S MOTHER WAS NOT VERY GOOD AT KEEPING SECRETS. WHEN SHE WENT TO FETCH THE WATER BY THE RIVERSIDE, SHE TOLD THE OTHER WOMEN ABOUT HER SON'S DREAM, AND SOON, THE NEWS REACHED THE ROYAL EARS.

PHU-CHUNG HAD SUCH A STRANGE DREAM I LET ME TELL YOU ABOUT IT...

WHAT! HOW DARE HE DREAM OF TAKING MY PLACE? BRING THAT YOUNG IMP BEFORE ME!!!

CHAKA-GYALPO, UNDERSTANDABLY, GOT VERY ANGRY, AND SENT OUT HIS GUARDS.

HE TRAVELLED ACROSS MOUNTAIN RANGES, CROSSING THEM THROUGH HIGH DESERTED PASSES.

HE GAINED EXPERIENCE AND WISDOM WITH EACH PASSING DAY. HE BECAME STRONG, AND LEARNT HOW TO SURVIVE THE WILDERNESS.

PHU-CHUNG ALSO LEARNT THE VALUE OF HIS MOTHER'S GIFTS —THE KNIFE AND THE BAG.

TIC! TIC!

AAH! BLESS YOU MOTHER!

AMONG OTHER USEFUL ARTICLES SUCH AS A NEEDLE AND THREAD, THE BAG ALSO CONTAINED A SMALL FLINT. WHEN THIS WAS STRUCK SHARPLY AGAINST THE METAL CLASP, IT GAVE OFF SPARKS WHICH COULD THEN LIGHT A SMALL FIRE.

SOMETIMES HE WOULD COME ACROSS MONASTERIES, LONELY AND IMPOSING IN THE VAST LANDSCAPE.

THE MONKS IN THE MONASTERIES WERE ALWAYS KIND, AND GAVE HIM A BOWL OF TSAMPA FOR DOING A FEW ODD JOBS IN THE KITCHEN.

AFTER WHICH, IT WAS THE LONG ROAD AGAIN...

ONE DAY, AFTER MANY YEARS OF WALKING, PHU-CHUNG REACHED A BEAUTIFUL LAKE. HE STOOD STILL FOR A MOMENT AND MARVELLED AT THE BEAUTY OF THIS CRYSTAL LAKE. HE DECIDED TO HAVE A CLOSER LOOK AND WALKED DOWN TO ITS EDGE.

HE TOOK OFF ONE BOOT AND LOOKED AT ITS SOLE; THERE WAS STILL NO CHANGE IN IT.

HE HAD ENOUGH OF THE BOOT BY NOW, AND HE THREW IT INTO THE LAKE IN DISGUST. THE BOOT SANK LIKE A STONE, WHICH WAS NOT SURPRISING.

HE THEN TOOK OFF THE OTHER BOOT ALSO, AND WAS WONDERING WHAT TO DO WITH IT WHEN—

SUDDENLY, A WHITE SNAKE SHOT OUT OF THE LAKE, FIGHTING FIERCELY WITH ANOTHER FIERCE BLACK SNAKE. THEIR HEADS WERE BATHED IN FIRE AS THEY REARED AND STRUCK AT EACH OTHER. PHU-CHUNG COULD BARELY BREATHE AS HE WATCHED!

HISSSS!

HISSS!

PHU-CHUNG INSTINCTIVELY PICKED UP HIS REMAINING BOOT — TOOK CAREFUL AIM, AND...

...THREW THE BOOT AT THE BLACK SNAKE. BOTH THE BOOT AND THE BLACK SNAKE SANK TO THE BOTTOM OF THE LAKE.

CLONK!

HE THEN WADED INTO THE WATER AND GENTLY PICKED UP THE WHITE SNAKE...

...AND PLACED IT INSIDE HIS WARM KHO WHERE IT REGAINED CONSCIOUSNESS.

GLUB! GLUB! GLUB!

SUDDENLY, THE LAKE BEGAN TO BUBBLE...

DO NOT BE AFRAID, PHU-CHUNG! YOU SHALL NOT BE HARMED. WE HAVE COME TO THANK YOU FOR SAVING OUR PRINCE. WE ALSO WANT TO INVITE YOU TO OUR WORLD BENEATH THIS LAKE WHERE THE DAGGER PEOPLE LIVE. WILL YOU COME?

BUT HOW CAN I DO THAT? I WILL SURELY DROWN UNDERWATER!

OH, DO NOT WORRY ABOUT THAT— JUST CLOSE YOUR EYES AND SAY— "I WANT TO BE THERE," AND YOU WILL BE WITH US IN OUR DAGGER WORLD.

PHU-CHUNG FOUND HIMSELF IN A BEAUTIFUL PALACE WITH MANY SERVANTS ATTENDING ON HIM. THERE WAS PLENTY TO EAT AND DRINK.

17

NOW LISTEN VERY CAREFULLY — I'VE NEVER TOLD ANYONE ABOUT THIS. I KNOW HOW TO KEEP A SECRET...I AM NOT LIKE OLD MRS DECHEN WHO CANNOT KEEP FROM GOSSIPING. IF YOU WANT TO KNOW THE LATEST NEWS FROM LHASA TO BEIJUNG, SHE'LL BE SURE TO KNOW...

YES, YES — BUT WHAT ABOUT THE SECRET?

OH, YES! GOOD YOU REMINDED ME. THESE DAGGERS POSSESS THREE VERY IMPORTANT ITEMS. THEY ARE, A BLANKET, A STAFF, AND A PUPPY DOG. IT IS THESE GIFTS WHICH MAKES THEM ALL POWERFUL.

SO?

SO YOU MUST ASK FOR THESE THREE ITEMS, DOPEY! THEY CANNOT REFUSE YOU BECAUSE YOU SAVED THEIR PRINCE!

OH!! I HAD NOT THOUGHT OF THAT.

WHEN YOU LEAVE, THEY WILL OFFER YOU GREAT WEALTH. YOU MUST REFUSE, AND INSTEAD, ASK FOR THE BLANKET, THE STAFF AND THE LITTLE PUP.

ARE YOU LISTENING?

YES, YES.

...BUT THERE IS ANOTHER THING — A **FOURTH** ITEM THAT I WANT...

I WISH TO RETURN TO MY SURFACE WORLD.

AND ABOUT TIME TOO!

PHU-CHUNG WENT TO THE DAGGER PRINCE FOR HIS PERMISSION TO LEAVE.

PHU-CHUNG LA, YOU HAVE DONE MY PEOPLE A GREAT SERVICE BY SAVING MY LIFE. I AM FOREVER INDEBTED TO YOU. IF YOU EVER NEED MY HELP, JUST CALL AND I SHALL HELP YOU. AS A TOKEN OF OUR GRATITUDE, YOU MAY ASK FOR WHATEVER YOUR HEART DESIRES — IT WILL BE YOURS!

THANK YOU, PRINCE. YOU ARE INDEED VERY GENEROUS.

NOT KNOWING WHAT TO DO NEXT, PHU-CHUNG PROPPED UP THE BLANKET ON THE STAFF, AS A ROUGH SHELTER FOR THE NIGHT. TYING THE PUP TO THE STAFF, HE WENT IN SEARCH OF SOME FOOD.

WHEN HE RETURNED IN THE EVENING, HE WAS ASTOUNDED TO SEE A LARGE, SPACIOUS TENT PITCHED WHERE HE HAD LEFT THE BLANKET. THE SMALL PUP AND THE STAFF WERE NOWHERE TO BE SEEN.

INSIDE, A TABLE WAS LAID WITH A FINE FEAST. IN A CORNER, A WARM FIRE BURNED AND MORE FOOD WAS ON THE BOIL. HE COULDN'T BELIEVE HIS LUCK!

PHU-CHUNG ENJOYED THIS MYSTERIOUS HOSPITALITY FOR A FEW DAYS, BUT SOON, HE BEGAN TO WONDER—

SO THE NEXT DAY, HE PRETENDED TO GO OUT AS USUAL, BUT INSTEAD, HE HID BEHIND SOME ROCKS AND WATCHED...

23

THERE'S NO NEED TO BE AFRAID ANYMORE, LU-MOH — I'M HERE TO PROTECT YOU.

LU-MOH, I HAVE EVERYTHING A MAN COULD POSSIBLY WANT AND YET, THERE IS ONE THING I STILL DESIRE...

AND WHAT IS THAT?

I WISH TO INVITE CHAKA GYALPO TO OUR HOME. I KNOW HE DID NOT LIKE ME, BUT THAT WAS A LONG TIME AGO, AND HE IS STILL MY KING.

IF THAT IS YOUR WISH, THEN INVITE HIM BY ALL MEANS — BUT REMEMBER, DO NOT ASK ME TO GIVE HIM MANY HELP-INGS OF FOOD AND WINE.

THE TRADITIONAL INVITATION WAS PREPARED AND SENT TO THE KING WHO ACCEPTED MORE OUT OF CURIOSITY THAN GOOD WILL.

ON THE APPOINTED DAY, CHAKA GYALPO ARRIVED...

PHU-CHUNG! IT'S GOOD TO SEE YOU AGAIN. THANK YOU FOR YOUR INVI-TATION WHICH I WAS GLAD TO ACCEPT. WELL, WELL, YOU SEEM TO HAVE DONE VERY WELL...

I'LL SOON FIND OUT HOW YOU BECAME SO WEALTHY.

WELCOME TO MY HUMBLE HOME, YOUR MAJESTY.

BUT WHAT WAS LU-MOH UP TO IN THE KITCHEN?

26

LU-MOH HAD VERY CAREFULLY COVERED HER FACE WITH SOOT, SO THAT THE KING WOULD NOT BE ATTRACTED TO HER — OR SO SHE THOUGHT.

BUT AS SHE WORKED, HER SWEAT RAN DOWN AND WASHED OFF THE SOOT. THE KING SAW HOW BEAUTIFUL LU-MOH WAS

I WARNED YOU, — BUT IT'S STILL NOT TOO LATE. THERE IS A WAY WE CAN WIN THAT CRAFTY KING. NOW, LISTEN CAREFULLY...

THE WATER BEGAN TO BUBBLE...

27

A HAND HOLDING A STEAMING BOX EMERGED FROM THE LAKE. PHU-CHUNG REACHED OUT AND GRABBED IT.

ONE MEDIUM BOX COMING UP

AGAIN, HE COULD NOT RESIST A LOOK, AND OPENED THE BOX.

AND ALL THE PIGEONS, BUT FOR A FEW, FLEW OUT OF THE BOX. PHU-CHUNG CLOSED THE LID QUICKLY AND RAN HOME.

THE DAY OF THE CONTEST ARRIVED, AND SO DID CHAKA-GYALPO, WITH SIX OF HIS BEST MEN TO HELP HIM PICK THE GRAINS. PHU-CHUNG STOOD WITH HIS FAITHFUL LU-MOH BESIDE HIM, AND HIS BOX OF PIGEONS.

PHU-CHUNG, ARE YOU READY FOR THE CONTEST?

YES, I AM.

LET THE CONTEST *BEGIN*!

CHAKA-GYALPO HURLED A BAG OF GRAIN INTO THE AIR, SCATTERING THEM FAR AND WIDE, IN THE WIND!

IS THIS A GRAIN I SEE BEFORE ME?

PHU-CHUNG IMMEDIATELY RELEASED HIS PIGEONS, AND OF COURSE, THE PIGEONS PICKED UP THE GRAINS FAR QUICKER THAT THE KING'S MEN, (WHO HAD, NO DOUBT, BEEN HAND-PICKED, BUT WERE NOT VERY GOOD AT PICKING WITH THEIR HANDS!) PHU-CHUNG WON THE CONTEST— HANDS DOWN.

I SAW IT FIRST!

OUCH!

IF ONLY THE PEOPLE OF YOUR VILLAGE COULD SEE YOU NOW, — "KUNCHOK" —THEY WOULD SAY— "WE THOUGHT YOU WERE EARNING GLORY." THIS IS HOW I EARN GLORY? SHEESH! DROPPED IT AGAIN!!

C'MON TASHI, IT'S ONLY A GRAIN. YOU CAN DO IT...GENTLY NOW, CONCENTRATE...

NOPE!! WASN'T READY.

SO MANY MORE CONTESTS WERE HELD, TO GIVE THE KING AN EDGE OVER PHU-CHUNG. HOWEVER, THE KING LOST OF ALL THEM, ROYALLY.

CHAKA-GYALPO, THE SPOILSPORT, DID NOT ACCEPT THE CONTEST RESULTS.

CHAKA-GYALPO'S HORSE COMPLETED THE RACE WITHOUT HIM.

IN THE RIVER-JUMP, THE KING FELL SHORT BY A COUPLE OF FEET — ONE RIGHT AND ONE LEFT, TO BE MORE PRECISE!

GLUG!

GLUG!

WHILE IN THE SKILL WITH KNIVES, — THE LESS SAID, THE BETTER!

I WARNED YOUR MAJESTY NOT TO COME TOO CLOSE! THE BLEEDING SHOULD STOP NOW.

BLOOD?

SUDDENLY, CHAKA YELLED OUT A SINGLE WORD—

APOPO!

WHA—!?!

'APOPO'? THE KING SAID THAT? VERY GOOD! NOW GO AND ASK HIM IF HE LIKES 'APOPO'. IF HE SAYS 'YES', YOU MUST GO DOWN TO OUR LAKE. CALL UP THE KING OF THE DAGGERS AND ASK HIM...

...FOR THE MEDIUM BOX OF WEAPONS. NOT THE BIG ONE, NOT THE SMALL ONE, BUT THE MEDIUM BOX OF WEAPONS. DO NOT OPEN THE BOX, OTHERWISE YOUR LIFE COULD BE IN DANGER. SO BE CAREFUL. GO, NOW!

THANK YOU, YOUR MAJESTY, YOU CAN PUT THIS TOO ON MY TAB.

HURRY UP, AND TAKE IT! THIS ONE'S REAL HEAVY!

NOT KNOWING WHAT THE WORD MEANT, PHU-CHUNG ASKED LU-MOH WAS IT WAS ALL ABOUT.

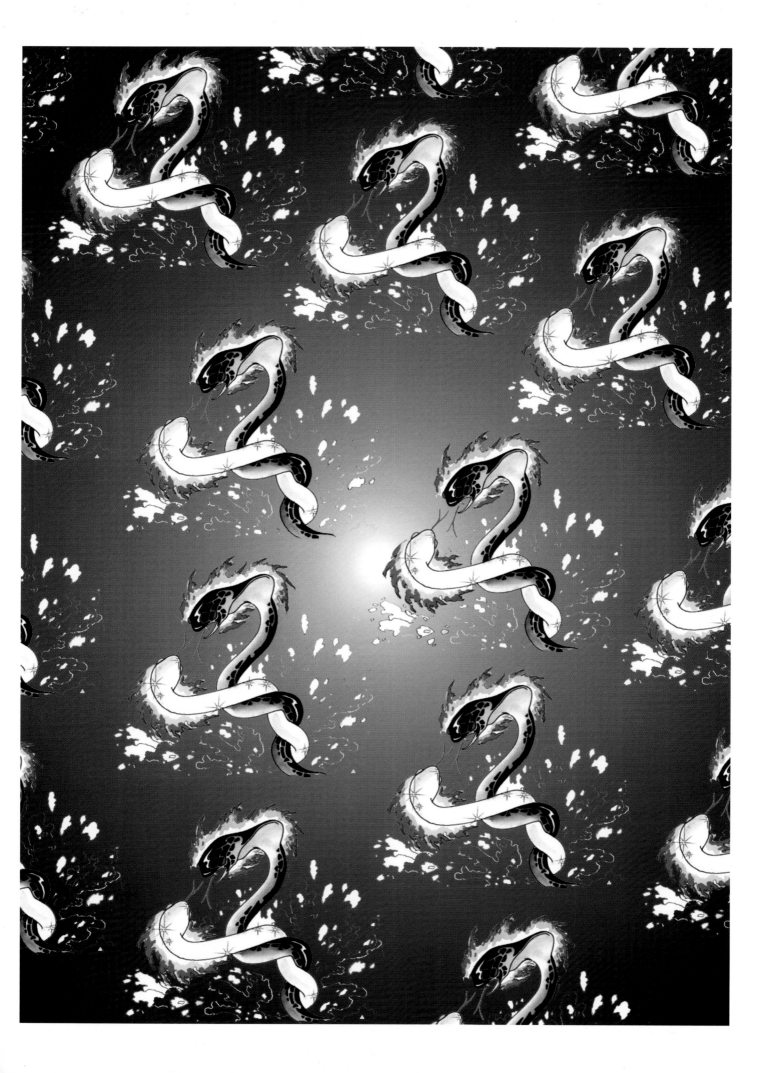

Copyright text and illustrations © Ringu Tulku 1995
First published 1995

ISBN 1 899171 10 X

Set in Technical by Simon Fraser, filmset by Posthouse Printing
Author photographs © Sunday Mail
Photograph of the Dalai Lama © The Office of Tibet
Cover Design by Simon Fraser
Printed and bound by Wing King Tong Co. Ltd., Hong Kong

Published by
Findhorn Press
The Park, Findhorn,
Forres IV36 OTZ, Scotland
tel 01309-690582 / fax 690036 / e-mail thierry@findhorn.org